ROGER RABBIT BABY HERMAN

"TUMMY TROUBLE"

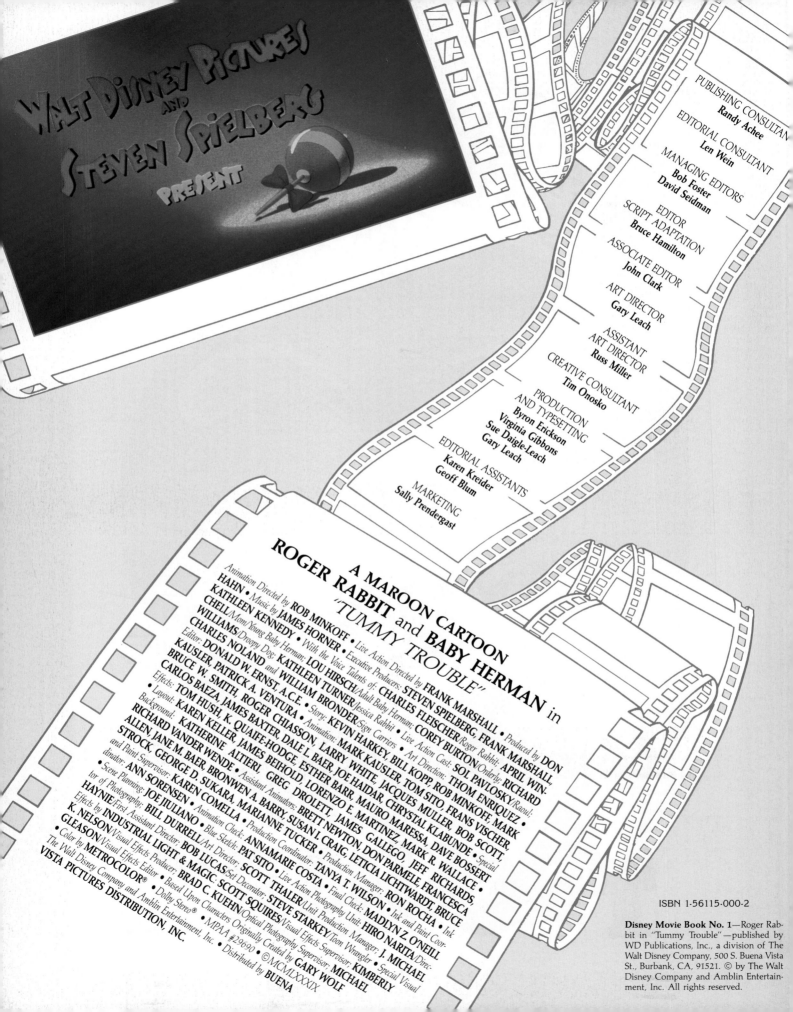

WALT DISNEY PICTURES AND STEVEN SPIELBERG PRESENT

PUBLISHING CONSULTANT
Randy Achee

EDITORIAL CONSULTANT
Len Wein

MANAGING EDITORS
Bob Foster
David Seidman

EDITOR
SCRIPT ADAPTATION
Bruce Hamilton

ASSOCIATE EDITOR
John Clark

ART DIRECTOR
Gary Leach

ASSISTANT
ART DIRECTOR
Russ Miller

CREATIVE CONSULTANT
Tim Onosko

PRODUCTION
AND TYPESETTING
Byron Erickson
Virginia Gibbons
Sue Daigle-Leach
Gary Leach

EDITORIAL ASSISTANTS
Karen Kreider
Geoff Blum

MARKETING
Sally Prendergast

A MAROON CARTOON
ROGER RABBIT and BABY HERMAN in
"TUMMY TROUBLE"

Animation Directed by ROB MINKOFF • Produced by DON HAHN • Music by JAMES HORNER • Live Action Directed by FRANK MARSHALL • Executive Producers: STEVEN SPIELBERG, FRANK MARSHALL, KATHLEEN KENNEDY • With the Voice Talents of: CHARLES FLEISCHER/Roger Rabbit; APRIL WINCHELL/Mom/Young Baby Herman; LOU HIRSCH/Adult Baby Herman; KATHLEEN TURNER/Jessica Rabbit; WILLIAMS/Droopy Dog • Live Action Cast: SOL PAVLOSKY/Raoul; COREY BURTON/Orderly; RICHARD WILLIAMS/Sign Carriers • Art Direction: THOM ENRIQUEZ • Editor: CHARLES NOLAND and WILLIAM BRONDER • Effects: DONALD W. ERNST • Story: KEVIN HARKEY, BILL KOPP, ROB MINKOFF, MARK KAUSLER, PATRICK A. VENTURA • Animation: MARK KAUSLER, BILL KOPP, DALE L. BAER, LARRY WHITE, JOE HAIDAR, JACQUES MULLER, TOM SITO, FRANS VISCHER, BOB SCOTT, BRUCE W. SMITH, ROGER CHIASSON, CARLOS BAEZA, JAMES BAXTER, ESTHER BAER, LORENZO E. MARTINEZ, MAURO MARESSA, MARK R. WALLACE, CHRYSTAL KLABUNDE, BRETT NEWTON, JAMES GALLEGO, JEFF RICHARDS, DON PARMELE, LETICIA LICHTWARDT, FRANCESCA ALLEN, JANE M. BAER, BRUCE STROCK • Assistant Animators: KATHERINE ALTIERI, RICHARD VANDER WENDE, KAREN KELLER, JAMES BEIHOLD, GREG DROLETT • Special Effects Animator: GEORGE D. SUKARA, BRONWEN A. BARRY, SUSAN I. CRAIG, MARIANNE TUCKER • Ink and Paint Supervisor: KAREN COMELLA • Production Coordinator: TANYA T. WILSON • Production Manager: RON ROCHA • Scene Planning: ANN SORENSEN • Animation Check: ANNAMARIE COSTA • Final Check: MADLYN Z. O'NEILL • Director of Photography: JOE JIULIANO • Blue Sketch: PAT SITO • Ink and Paint Coordinator: HAYNIE • First Assistant Director: BILL DURRELL • Art Director: BOB LUCAS • Live Action Photography Unit Production Manager: HIRO NARITA • Set Decorator: SCOTT THALER • Unit Production Manager: J. MICHAEL HAYNIE • Scott Squires • Visual Effects Supervisor: MICHAEL GLEASON • Toon Wrangler: KIMBERLY K. NELSON • Optical Photography Supervisor: STEVE STARKEY • Effects by INDUSTRIAL LIGHT & MAGIC • Visual Effects Editor: BRAD C. KUEHN • Visual Effects Producer: SCOTT SQUIRES • Color by METROCOLOR® • The Walt Disney Company and Amblin Entertainment • Based Upon Characters Originally Created by GARY WOLF • Dolby Stereo® • MPAA #29690 • ©MCMLXXXIX • Distributed by BUENA VISTA PICTURES DISTRIBUTION, INC.

ISBN 1-56115-000-2

Disney Movie Book No. 1—Roger Rabbit in "Tummy Trouble"—published by WD Publications, Inc., a division of The Walt Disney Company, 500 S. Buena Vista St., Burbank, CA, 91521. © by The Walt Disney Company and Amblin Entertainment, Inc. All rights reserved.

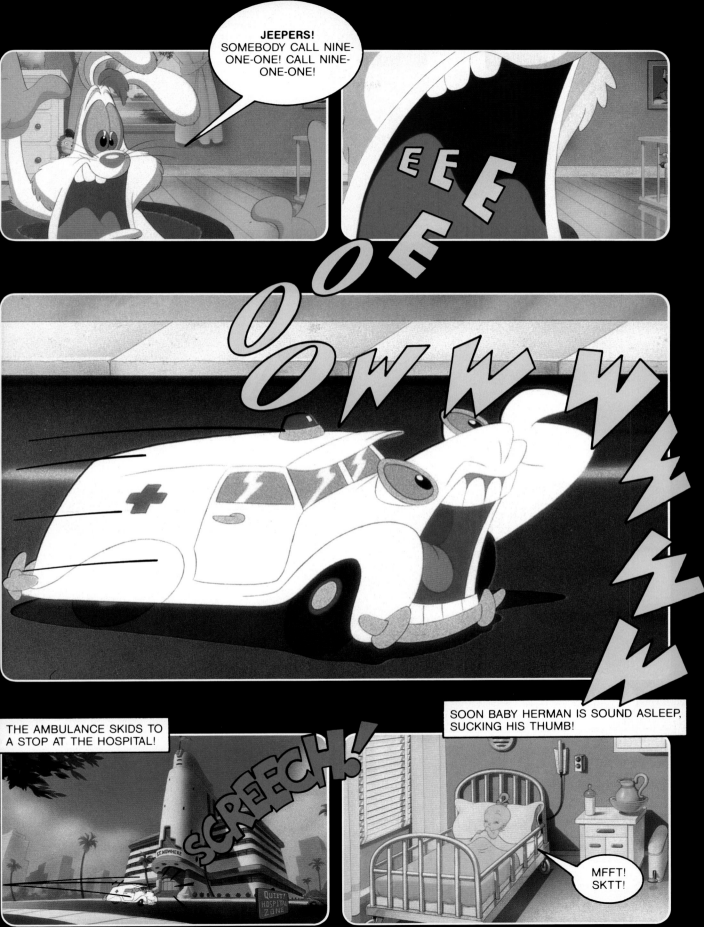

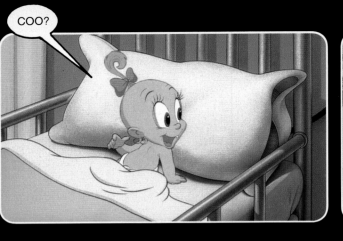

COO?

SUDDENLY, THE DOOR **BURSTS OPEN!**

PANT! PANT! PANT!

COO!

P-P-PLEASE BE OKAY, BABY HERMAN! WHY DOES EVERYTHING HAPPEN TO **YOU?**

WHY COULDN'T IT HAPPEN TO **ME?**

HUH?

TO **ME!**

ROGER ABSENT-MINDEDLY SNATCHES THE BABY BOTTLE!

GLUG!

SUCK!

GLUG!

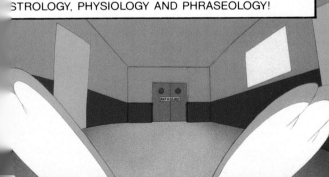

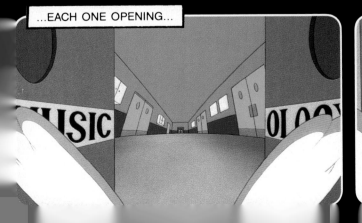

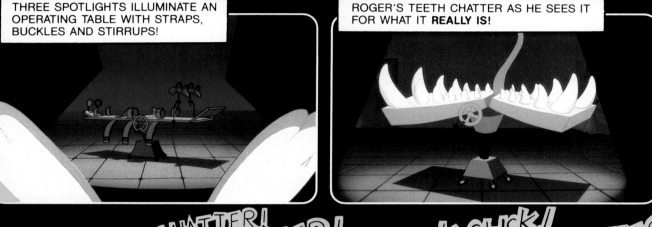
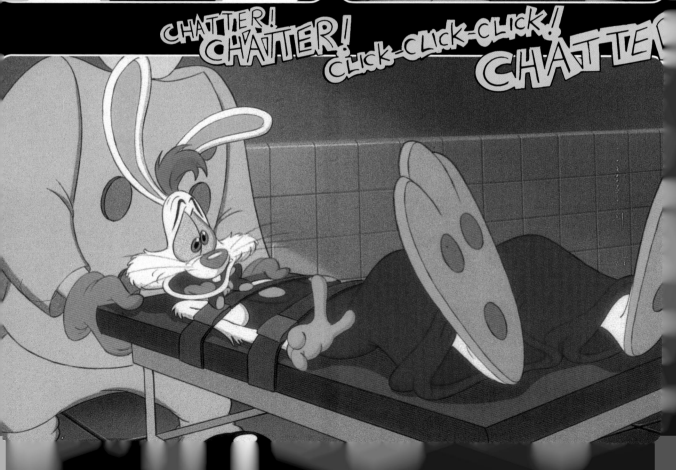

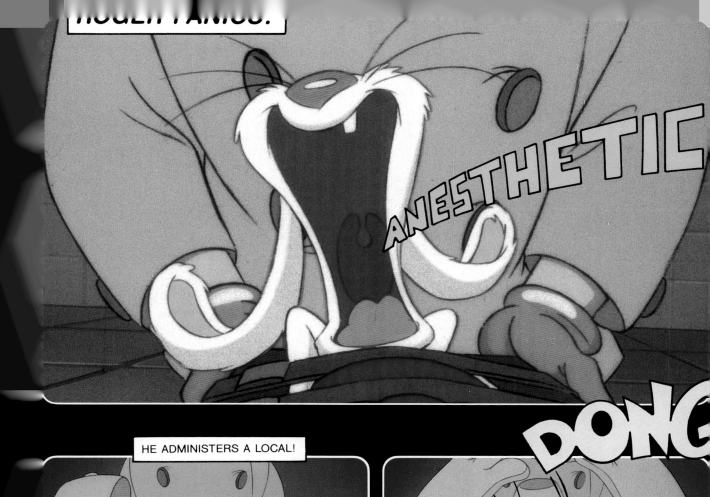

ANESTHETIC

DONG

HE ADMINISTERS A LOCAL!

BACK IN THE PEDIATRIC WARD, BABY HERMAN SPOTS THE DAY NURSE, **JESSICA RABBIT!**

COO!

BOTTLE!

PLOP!

OOF!

OOH, BOTTLE, BOTTLE, BOTTLE!

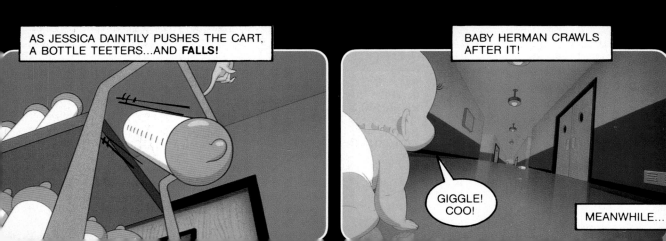

AS JESSICA DAINTILY PUSHES THE CART, A BOTTLE TEETERS...AND **FALLS!**

BABY HERMAN CRAWLS AFTER IT!

GIGGLE! COO!

MEANWHILE...

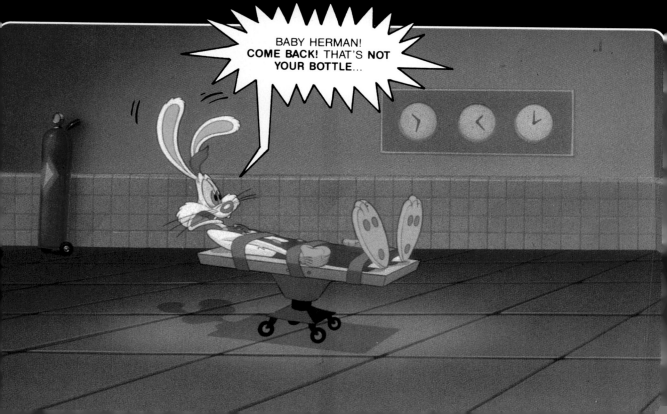

WEEEE...

...EEEE!

SPROI-OI-OING!

BABY HERMAN IS CATAPULTED TO THE CEILING, WHERE HE LANDS ON THE NOSE OF A **SURGICAL LASER!**

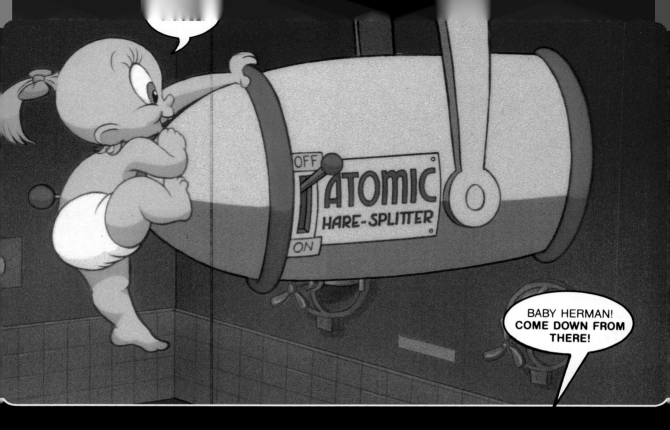

BABY HERMAN! **COME DOWN FROM THERE!**

IT'S **DANGEROUS!**

CLICK!

YAH-H-H-H!

THE LASER **MISSES** ROGER, BUT **BLASTS** AN OXYGEN TANK...

...AND **UNLEASHES** A BARRAGE OF **HYPODERMIC** NEEDLES...

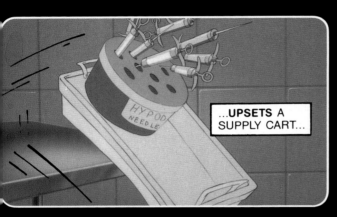

...**UPSETS** A SUPPLY CART...

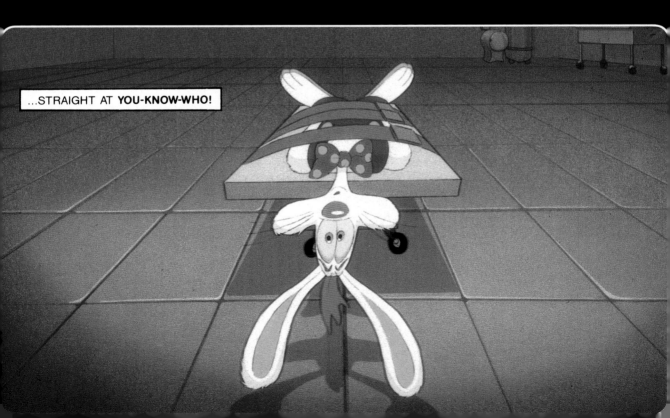

...STRAIGHT AT **YOU-KNOW-WHO!**

YEEEEEEEEEEEEOWW

UHHHH!

OOP!

WHIT! WHIT!

WHIT!

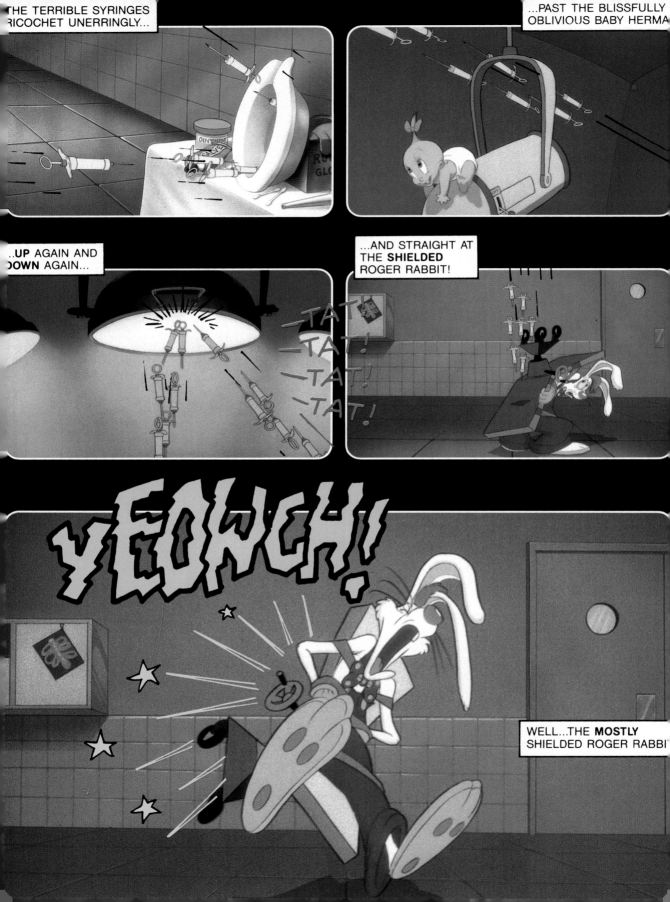

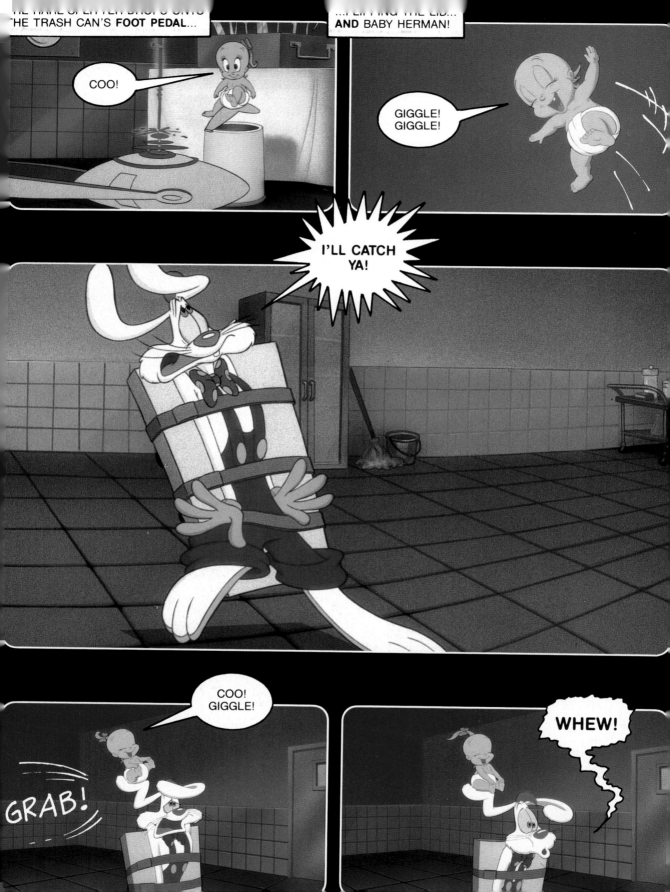

THE HARE-SPLITTER—STILL FIRING—**TILTS OVER**...

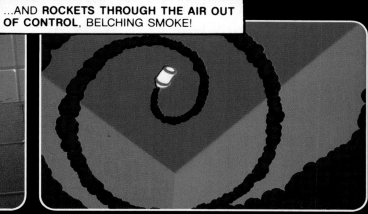

...AND **ROCKETS THROUGH THE AIR OUT OF CONTROL**, BELCHING SMOKE!

HUH?

THE FEARSOME PROJECTILE PLOWS INTO ROGER...

SQUEAL!

UGHH!

...AND BABY AND BABYSITTER ARE OFF AGAIN!

ZOOM!

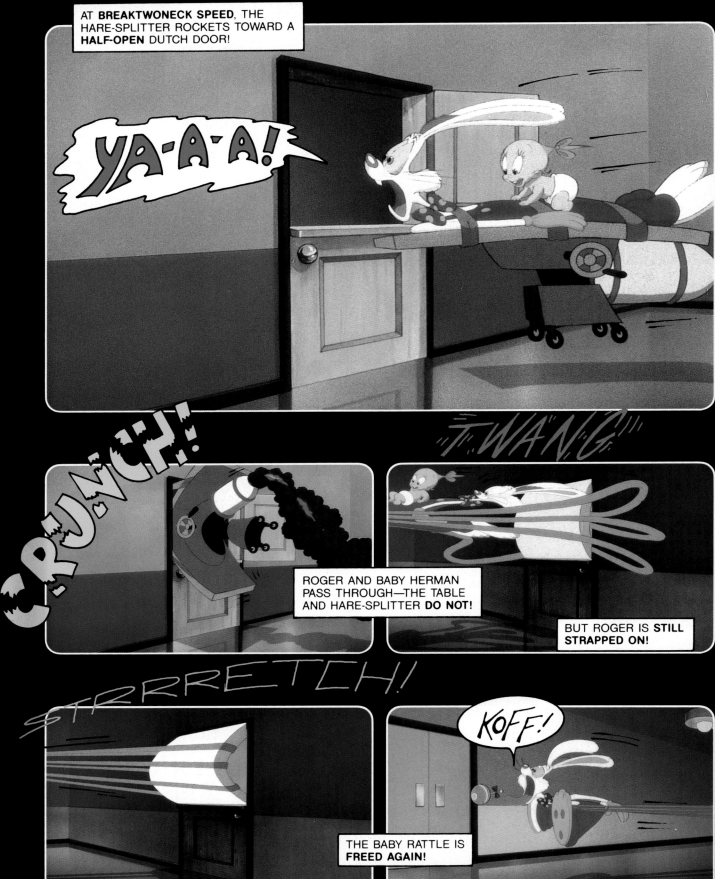

THE WHEELCHAIR SCREECHES TO A **HALT!**

SCREECH!

BUT ITS PASSENGERS **DO NOT!**

YE-E-O-O-W-W!

GIGGLE!

ROGER QUICKLY PRESSES HIS FEET AGAINST THE SIDES OF THE ELEVATOR SHAFT AND **STOPS HIS DESCENT!**

SQUEEK!

SQUEEK!

THEN HE SNATCHES BABY HERMAN!

WHOO!

GOT YA!

THE ERRANT RATTLE WHISTLES BY!

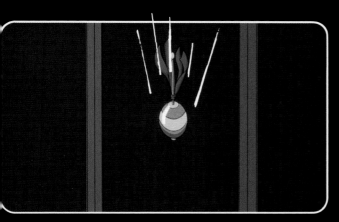

...BOUNCES BACK...

THE RATTLE HITS BOTTOM...

...AND IS **SWALLOWED AGAIN** BY BABY HERMAN!

YOWW!

GULP!

STARTLED, ROGER **LOSES** HIS GRIP...

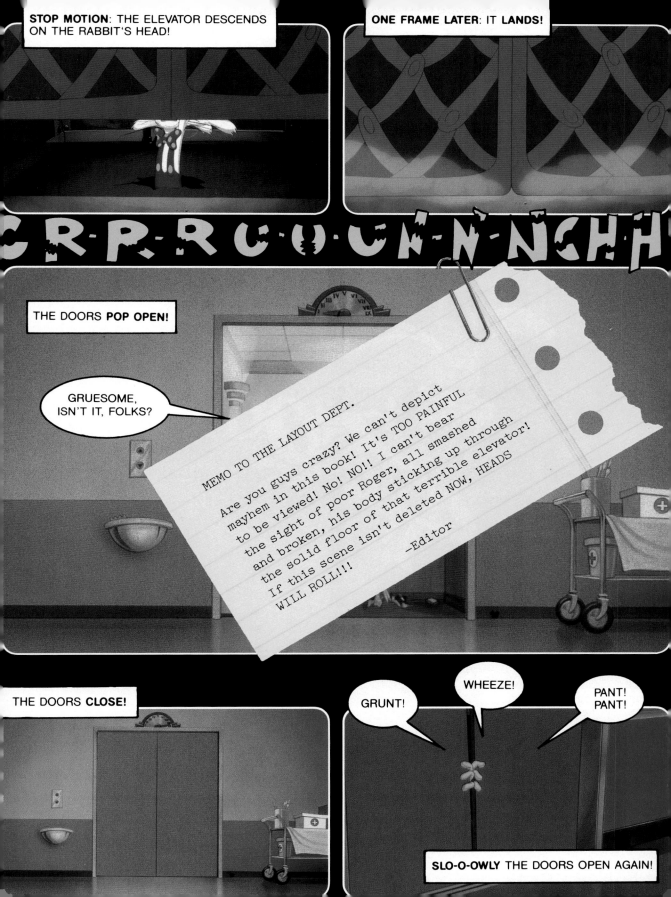

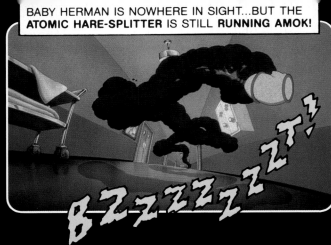

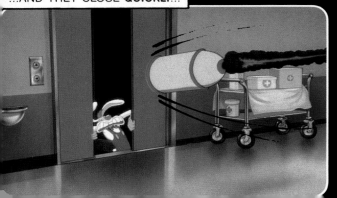

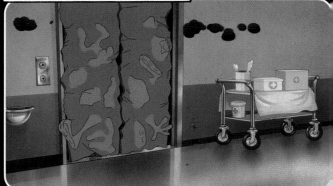

GROAN!

EASY DOES IT...

COO!

GIGGLE!

AH, BABY HERMAN, IT LOOKS LIKE **SMOOTH SAILING** FROM NOW ON!

COO!

GASP!

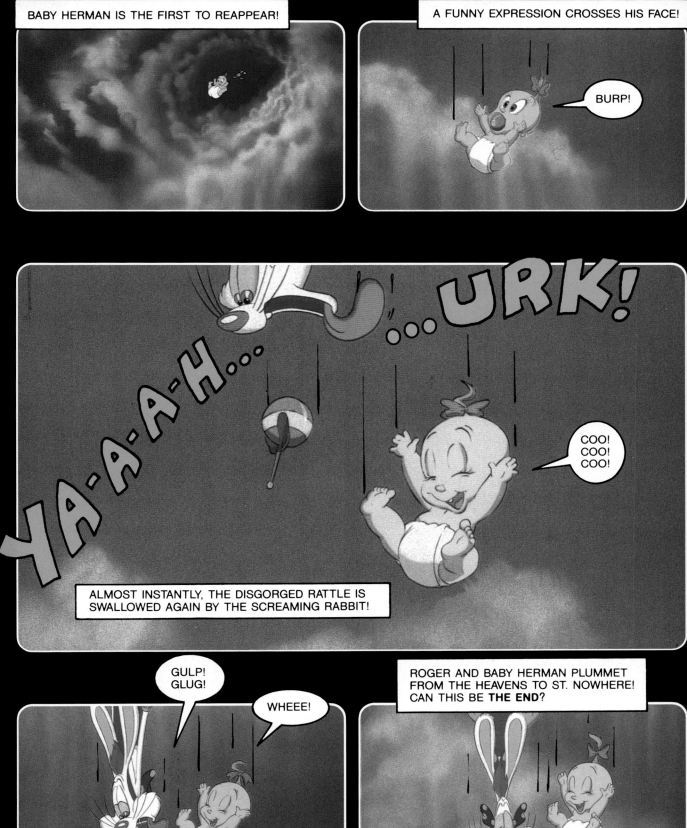

WHAM!

GRUNT!

ROGER HITS THE **ROOF**...AND PASSES THROUGH!

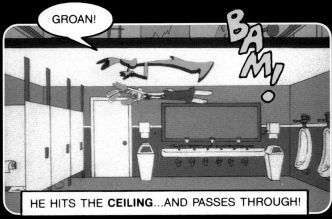

GROAN!

BAM!

HE HITS THE **CEILING**...AND PASSES THROUGH!

ELEVEN STORIES LATER, THE MARBLE FLOOR OF THE LOBBY BREAKS HIS FALL!

OOF!

SPLAT!

GASP!

WHERE'S BABY HERMAN?

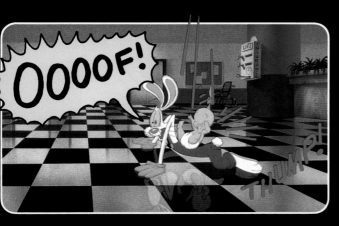

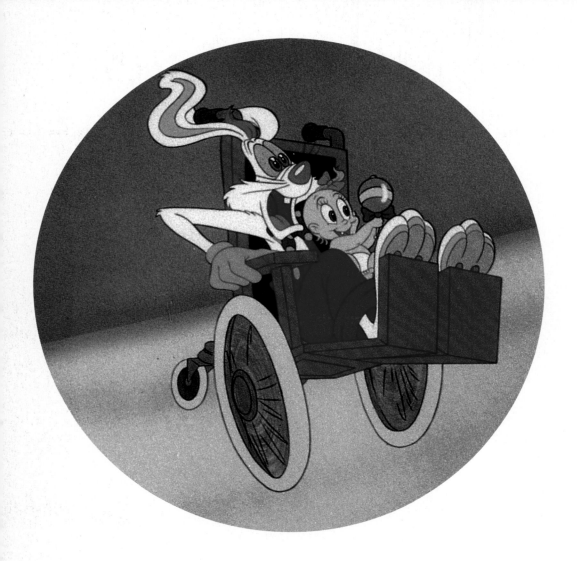

BEHIND THE SCENES

Interviews with the men who made "Tummy Trouble"

What did it take to make "Tummy Trouble"? The film's creators answer: a million babies, putting oneself in a flux place, and some gasps for air, among other things.

Writer Jim Fanning interviewed director Rob Minkoff, writer-animator Mark Kausler, writers Bill Kopp, Pat Ventura, and Kevin Harkey, and the voice of Roger Rabbit himself, Charles Fleischer. He asked them about the making of "Tummy Trouble" and about the inspiration that went into it. The creators also tell Fanning about their careers before "Tummy Trouble" and about work that you'll be seeing in the future—including the next Roger short, "Roller Coaster Rabbit."

Interview with Rob Minkoff

Q. How did you get into animation?

A. I went to Cal Arts and got hired in 1983 by Disney. The summer before that I was an intern for a month, and I got to work with Eric Larson, one of Walt Disney's "Nine Old Men." [When I was officially hired,] I was an in-betweener on **The Black Cauldron**. Then I got to do character designs on **Great Mouse Detective**, became an animator, and then got to be a supervising animator on that show.

Q. What followed that?

A. I worked in development for a while, writing, and did a little animation for different smaller projects like the Mickey Mouse/Tom Selleck Academy Awards presentation. And [then there was] the Donald Duck/Richard Dreyfuss TV special about the constitution that I did a couple of scenes on. I also wrote a couple of scripts and actually co-wrote a song that's in **Oliver and Company**.

Q. How did you become the director of "Tummy Trouble"?

A. As a result of my work in development, when that project came down the pipeline, I got put in charge of developing possible Roger Rabbit stories. We did two storyboards.

The presentation was very interesting. Mark Kausler pitched "Hare in My Soup," and I got "Tummy Trouble." I sweated a lot and gasped for air a lot. It's exhausting! If you've seen the cartoon, you know it's pretty breakneck.

Q. How did you go from story development to being a director?

A. At that same pitch meeting, [the executives] made us leave the room and talked about it. Then I got called in and was told I was going to be director.

Q. How did you feel about that?

A. I was wildly ecstatic! But I tried to keep my head.

Q. What were some of the challenges directing "Tummy Trouble"?

A. Well, there was severe time pressure! I heard from someone in management that they really didn't think we could get it done on time. They were surprised that it *did* get done on time! We were battling pressure and my own inexperience, trying to match the quality of "Somethin's Cooking," the original Roger [short] in **Who Framed Roger Rabbit**, which was pretty outstanding.

Q. What was the schedule on "Tummy Trouble"?

A. We were given a ten-week rotating schedule—meaning ten weeks for each of the processes—so [we got] ten weeks for animation, [but] I think we definitely went over that. All told I think it ended up being four months total for production. We were trying to keep the quality level [high].

Q. Besides the original **Roger Rabbit** opener, what were some of the influences or inspirations you drew on?

A. Tex Avery and Bob Clampett set the tone for the original movie. They were directors of cartoon shorts in the 1940's. Clampett's style was crazy, unrelenting and really wacky, whereas Avery would usually make a gag out of twisting logic and making a point of it. Clampett's [work] was more like the loon—like [he used] Daffy Duck as just a crazy, obnoxious sort of character. Clampett handled him that way as opposed to, say, Chuck Jones, who made the characters a bit more intelligent.

Q. What was Steven Spielberg's input?

A. He would give us comments and ideas, suggestions. He gave us a bunch of notes from the beginning, and we continually showed him the reel as production progressed. He would continually add new ideas.

Q. What was fun about working with the character of Roger Rabbit?

A. The fact that he was literally a cartoon character you could do anything with. He was malleable.

Q. Not many of those around anymore, are there?

A. There are not. And Disney certainly has never done one, so this is a first. It's fun to make Roger's eyes bulge out to become twice their size and to do the kinds of things you can't do with Mickey Mouse. [But] it's really easy with Roger to go too far because he wants to do everything bigger and more to the extreme than other characters.

Q. How was it working with Charlie Fleischer?

A. It was always entertaining. Charlie is just as crazy as Roger is. He constantly ad-libbed, on and off mike.

Q. How do you feel about the success of "Tummy Trouble"?

A. For a long time animators wondered about how the American public perceived the whole art form of animation, and whether what we were doing was a lost cause. I think people really seem to want to see more and that in and of itself is really rewarding and satisfying. It makes me feel good about having chosen this path.

Q. Will you comment on what this might mean for the future of cartoon shorts?

A. I think "Tummy Trouble" has proven that cartoon shorts can be an asset to a [feature] film release, which I think is important. If the next one comes out and it does well, then I really think it could spark a resurgence of theatrical shorts.

Q. Now you're directing the next **Roger Rabbit** cartoon.

A. Right. "Roller Coaster Rabbit." It takes place in an amusement park. The roller coaster is the biggest and most terrifying that has ever been ridden!

Q. Do you have any comments about working in Florida at the Disney MGM Studios animation department?

A. Well, there are about 300 [park guests] who look at [you] about every five minutes—300 new faces. It's an unusual experience.

Q. Do you ever get any feedback from those people or encounter them?

A. Yes, sometimes! They're very excited about [animation]. I was at the video, which is right under the window, and as I was looking through a scene, I turned around. Somebody was tapping on the window. It was a little kid about 12 years old, and he had a sign he had written that said, "Future Animator—Please Let Me In."

Interview with Mark Kausler

Q. Would you begin by telling us what your background is?

A. I worked at virtually every studio around from 1968 until 1985, when I started working on **Who Framed Roger Rabbit**. My background has basically been freelance animation. I did a lot of commercials during those years, and worked on **Yellow Submarine**. I worked

Consecutive frames within the footage of a live-action film usually show only a small change in movement. In animated cartoons, however, the humor is sometimes accentuated by the suddenness of a drastic change from one frame to the next.

for Ralph Bakshi on **Heavy Traffic** and **Coonskin**, and I worked a lot for Warner Brothers. I was on staff for a while with Duck Soup Productions of Santa Monica and did a lot of commercials with them— the Fruit Loops' toucan and a lot of stuff like that.

I haven't been with Disney a terribly long time. I started there on **Oliver and Company**, I think, two or three years ago. Then I left **Oliver** to go on to the animation of **Who Framed Roger Rabbit**.

I worked on the Toontown sequence and I did Droopy, Tweety, Benny the Cab, and a lot of other characters. I went back to work on **Oliver** for three weeks but then was laid off. Then I worked— not directly for Disney—but outside for Bob Rogers and Company. We made **Back to Neverland**, which is the Robin Williams/Walter Cronkite short they're running at the Florida animation studio.

After that I went to work on "Tummy Trouble." I went into story, did a whole lot of sketches for it and helped to develop the picture. [When] it went into animation, I stayed with it.

Q. Are you working on "Roller Coaster Rabbit," too?

A. Yeah. I'm animating on that. Actually, I'm doing some story work, too. I alternate between animation and story.

Q. Had you worked with Richard Williams before **Roger Rabbit**?

A. No, but I knew him pretty well. I've known him for quite a lot of years, as a matter of fact. We used to write letters back and forth years ago. We almost worked together on **Raggedy Ann** but couldn't strike a deal.

Q. Did you animate Roger Rabbit himself in **Who Framed Roger Rabbit**?

A. Yes, I did! But in only one shot. It was where he's talking to Benny the Cab. Benny's limping along on his two wheels and Roger says, "Benny, is that you?" And then Benny says, "Move over, Roger, you've done enough driving for one night." That was the one little scene I got to do of Roger.

Q. How did your involvement with "Tummy Trouble" begin?

A. In "Tummy Trouble," I started by

doing storyboards. I was hired as a story-board artist, and we were developing another picture with Roger in a restaurant. We had several other choices. We had Roger in a restaurant, and one in a circus, and then we wound up doing him in a hospital. That was the picture that finally got picked because Bob Zemeckis thought the setting of a hospital was funny and Steven Spielberg liked it, too. Spielberg picked the hospital because he thought children could relate more to a hospital setting than to a restaurant. So "Tummy Trouble" was [begun], and I started animating on it under Rob Minkoff, who was our director.

Q. Did you work on all the characters or primarily on Roger?

A. I didn't do Jessica because she was only in a few shots. But I had to do Baby Herman and Roger, basically. I also animated a surgeon who was chasing Roger. Roger dives into a medicine chest; the surgeon pulls on his tail; and [Roger] says, "Hey, let go of the cotton, you swab," beeps his nose and runs away. That was my scene. I did that shot. I wrote the line and the whole bit.

And I did a lot on the elevator sequence, where they fall down an elevator shaft, Baby swallows a rattle, Roger falls to the floor of the shaft, and Droopy is the elevator boy.

Q. Do you enjoy working with Droopy and other classic characters?

A. Oh, it's great! I've always enjoyed drawing them, just kind of fooling around. This was a chance to do it and actually see it get used. That was a big kick!

Q. What were and are the challenges and the fun parts of working with or animating Roger Rabbit?

A. Well, the challenge is in trying to get the Disney side of him to work with the Tex Avery side. He's a combination of

so many things. He has his cute aspects and he's also wacky, so sometimes it's hard to do both at the same time. That's what's difficult to keep—that hybrid tone that he has. I prefer him to be more wacky myself, but every once in a while you're forced to tone him down and to make him cuter so he works better with the baby and the other characters.

Q. When he's real wacky and bugging his eyes out, screaming and doing big takes, is that the fun part of it for you?

A. Yeah, that's more fun. The subdued stuff is a little harder to control for me, but it's getting better. I'm getting used to it now. [Baby Herman] has become a super Disney character. He started out crazy. In Dick Williams' version, [he] was more wacky, but he's gotten rounder and his proportions more natural. He's [closer to] a real baby now than he was in the feature.

Q. Do you mean in the cartoon that opens **Who Framed Roger Rabbit**? That obviously served as the model for "Tummy Trouble."

A. Yes. We were trying to get that flavor as much as we could in "Tummy Trouble," but with a lot less time and budget to work with.

Q. Would you explain what that flavor is?

A. It's [like a] forties cartoon on amphetamines! It's a lot faster and a lot more in your face than the real forties cartoons were because they didn't have the budgets or care expended on them that "Somethin's Cooking" had.

Q. Is it an advantage for an animator to be involved in the story?

A. Actually, all animators are involved in the story, whether officially or not, because it's the nature of the job. The animator is the storyteller. You take what

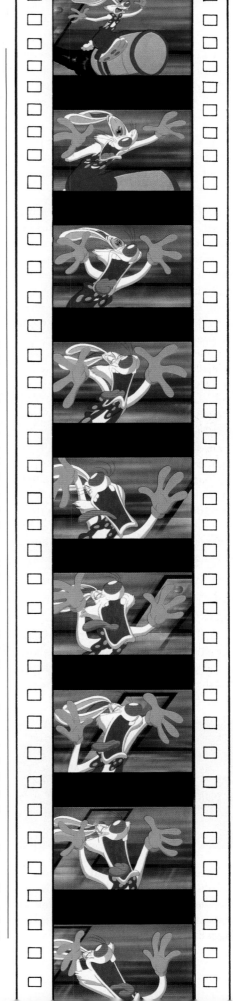

somebody else has written or drawn and make it live! You make it move and hopefully communicate all the story points, and if you don't understand the story, then you're at a big disadvantage.

Q. You were under a lot of time pressure on "Tummy Trouble." Do you care to talk about that and the challenges it presented?

A. I didn't really feel it that much myself because I'm used to working under deadlines from years and years of doing freelance work. That's all freelance work is: meeting a deadline and getting a product out. So it wasn't really that hard for me. I got to do each scene several times to get it as good as it could be done.

I guess the real challenge was in what we call the post-production phase where they had to do all the cels, backgrounds, and everything else really, really fast. They had to cheat a little, like on some of the long shots. They had to leave out some of the color separations that in the feature they probably would have [left in], but because of [a lack of] time they had to leave out a few colors and simplify stuff. But on the close-ups they left them all in. Actually, it's pretty hard to tell the difference, especially when something's moving really fast.

Q. Were there any funny little things that happened, or interesting stories connected with your work?

A. It's hard to tell anecdotes because not all that much went on that is related to the production that was funny. It was just the things we did to take the pressure

Animators have never been able to resist inside jokes. They often throw in references to someone on signs that pass by quickly on painted backgrounds.

off of ourselves, such as dressing up like different characters or imitating voices.

Most of our laughs we get [now are] by making fun of the soundtrack. We latch onto a word or [a sound] like Roger screaming all the time in "Tummy Trouble." We're always trying to scream like Roger, running up and down the halls, doing anything to take the pressure off, because sometimes it gets pretty intense. You start acting like a nut and it helps. But basically [the work is] pretty straightforward. Once the story is done, you just have to make the picture.

It's not like live action in that you don't work with a lot of talent, except in the case of Charlie Fleischer, who's an absolute nut. That guy is really crazy to work with because he has no respect for what you've written. I tried to write all this dialogue for Roger and he said, "Roger wouldn't say that. I can't say that. Who wrote this?" I said, "I did." He was embarrassed when he realized the person that wrote it was sitting in the room right next to him. He's a real funny guy.

Special effects abound in "Tummy Trouble." An electrical shock Roger receives leaves the room dark for an instant, but one can still discern a jagged outline of the rabbit.

Interview with Bill Kopp, Pat Ventura, and Kevin Harkey

Q. The first thing we need to know is the background of each of you. Bill?

Bill: Well, I did a couple of student films and I worked on [a few] features, [including] **One Crazy Summer**. I worked on **The Tracey Ullman Show** and **The Late Show** for Fox, and now I'm here.

Pat: I've been working the past nine or ten years now in the industry. I've done everything from animation to storyboards to character development, and a number of TV shows. In particular, I've done design work for Hanna-Barbera and everywhere else.

Kevin: I've been at Disney on and off. Eventually, I came back just to do clean-up on **Oliver and Company**. I wanted to get into story development because I've done it on the outside. I was brought

The storyboard artists are the "writers" who work on cartoons, scripting dialog along with their sketches.

in as an intern on a Mickey Mouse featurette and then I was put on the Rogers.

Q. You guys have formed a real team here.

Bill: Yeah, we work together really well on these Rogers. [Besides,] you can tell when a cartoon kind of writes itself that you've got a good idea. If it's not working, you can't make it work, you know. We went through that. But once you get a good idea, it puts itself together. Good gags.

Kevin: Originally, two stories were developed—"Tummy Trouble" and "Hare in my Soup" with Roger as a waiter. We presented them to the bigwigs, and they decided to go with the hospital one because everyone can relate to that better.

Bill: "Tummy Trouble" is a frenetically paced cartoon. It is faster and there is more going on. It's more suited to what people would remember from the feature,

The quick, fluid style of the storyboard artists lent itself well to the slam-bang action of "Tummy Trouble."

than [if we had] branched off into something that might not be in character for Roger. It's more slam-bang.

Q. What inspiration did you draw from the original cartoon in the feature?

Bill: It kept coming up. We'd look at the cartoon a lot.

Kevin: Over and over.

Bill: Working on "Roller Coaster Rabbit" was the same thing. It always came back to that cartoon. "Look how they did this and look how they did that." Storywise, we didn't feel any pressure, [but there was] more when it came to putting it up on reels and looking at it and getting into layout.

Pat: And there were tons of gags. We

kept whittling them away, trying to get down to the main story.

Bill: You always have more than you need. You have to "murder a darling" because it's just not working, and you have to cut it. We did that until we got it down to the funniest stuff.

Kevin: At one point [we had] Baby Herman leading a bunch of other babies through and out the hospital.

Pat: Yeah, we had a million babies! We had a great gag with a nurse on a bulldozer, scooping up millions of babies!

Bill: It was a great collection of different gags, but it didn't blend as a whole, and we realized Roger and Baby Herman are the funniest when they're

together. It seems to help the pace of the cartoon. If you get too big and convoluted, it seems to lose some gas.

Pat: Two or three days before the big meeting with Spielberg we looked at it and we said it's not working. We had two or three days to shape it up.

Bill: Yeah, we've done that a lot. Sometimes when we're in a pinch, it seems to do something to force your head into thinking of gags that work. "Now you're going to be funny, and you're going to be funny really fast."

Pat: In the middle of "Tummy Trouble" they sent us to St. Joseph's Hospital in Burbank to their O.R.

Bill: Yeah, that was interesting. It didn't really deliver any gags, but it was weird to look at what those people do for a living and what we do for a living.

Pat: We took a real hospital and twisted it into what we wanted.

Kevin: You'll never find a laser drill suspended from the ceiling in a real hospital.

Q. Tell us about your sources of inspiration.

Kevin: We looked at a lot of old Bob Clampett and Tex Avery cartoons.

Pat: We looked at all [types of] MGM cartoons, Looney Tunes, and all that funny stuff.

Bill: What Roger is really spoofing is the old cartoons! It's a comment on the old animation. It's not like taking gags from old cartoons and putting them in the new ones. The old cartoons inspired us to create new gags.

Q. Were you under a lot of time pressure?

Bill: I [don't] remember feeling that we just had to get this thing done. They left us alone because they knew that was the only way. Nobody knew what to tell us to do, but *you* know when it's not working and *you* know when it is! I think that "Roller Coaster" has got a really strong structure that's been the model that I keep in my head as I look at subsequent storyboards. Of course, at the end, "Roller Coaster" has a big socko finish. I think it's going to be great.

Kevin: I feel "Coaster" is the best one. Now they're trying to branch off Roger into a different type of formula. It's not Roger and Baby. It'll be interesting to see how it works out.

Bill: I think we're working with Roger's personality more.

Q. Do you also think you're developing his character more?

The rattle going down Baby Herman's throat had to be modified to work well in the film's animation, in contrast to the funnier storyboard drawing above.

In a Maroon Cartoon, when a toon gulps down something—as seen here when Baby Herman first swallows his rattle—the object in question goes down like an orange stretching through a rubber hose.

Pat: Oh, yeah! We're working on him every day.

Bill: Now we can tell when something's out of character. Before we [had developed] his character, we would try things and we couldn't say, well, they're definitely not in his character. Now it's really obvious [to us] when he's doing something that's in character and when he's not.

If he has to do anything that takes concentration or a task that goes on for too long, he'll definitely screw up.

Pat: Yeah. He's not like Sylvester or Wile E. Coyote, where they're the villains.

Bill: Yeah, Roger's not a predator at all.

Pat: Roger just tries to be helpful and he doesn't help at all.

Bill: Everything he touches turns to aluminum foil instead of gold.

Interview with Charles Fleischer

Q. How did you create Roger's voice?

A. Well, the process I used is the same process I use anytime I create a character, and it's perhaps analogous to painting, where you start with a sketch, then do a water color and finally an oil or acrylic or something that lasts permanently. It's based on fundamental aspects of the character you get from reading the script.

Q. Had you seen what Roger was going to look like?

A. They showed me a drawing of what Roger looks like, so I had to create a voice that sounded like it was coming out of a three-foot cartoon rabbit, which is definitely a vocal parameter. It couldn't be too deep or it couldn't be too high, and it couldn't be too annoying. It had to have a certain emotional center that would make him sympathetic to audiences.

Q. How would you describe the voice you do? What are the qualities that you're trying to convey?

A. Oh, well, I think there's a certain warmth and sincerity and a certain loony, irreverent quality, and the combination of those two emotions— "I'll do anything for a laugh" and "I really love you." He has a relationship with his wife that's based on true love, and I don't think that's been really discussed too much in the feature toon.

Q. Have you done cartoon voices before Roger?

A. No, I never have.

Q. So he was your first, huh?

A. Yeah, and I didn't think of it as a voice. I thought of it as a character. I don't really know how to do just a voice.

A. How much influence do you feel that your voice characterization had on the animation and the development of the character?

A. Well, they animate to the voice so certainly the vocal performance that you give is a blueprint on which they base their animation. So it's intrinsic to the process.

Q. I understand that you do quite a bit of ad-libbing. Can you talk about that?

A. Well, I Rogerize things. I try to make them as funny as possible or I will say, for instance, "Roger wouldn't say that," or "Roger wouldn't do that." And then if I give an example of what he does—and if it's better—they use it.

Q. And how is the recording of the voice actually done? Do you do it from a script or storyboards or what?

A. Well, there're two different methods that I've utilized.

Number one, when we were filming the feature, I was on the set every day, and I memorized my lines just like any actor would normally do. The only difference: I was off camera. I even wore a costume every day.

For the cartoon shorts, since there're no other actors involved, I just go into the studio and record the lines by myself, which in some instances is more difficult, because you don't have the atmosphere, the environment, the presence of other actors to stimulate your imagination when you're doing a performance.

It's more like radio except for the fact that you know the visual's coming. So in your mind you're trying to picture what the environment is. I have to sometimes close my eyes and just imagine being in the situation as Roger. You have to put yourself into this flux place where this toon world is possible and let your imagination take you to this place.

I think a psychiatrist might say that you could be committable if you do this stuff well. And, the thing is I really get into him. I'm really serious about it. I can joke about it now, but when I'm doing it, it's like, "Hey, man, I'm really into this." So it's very bizarre, but I really enjoy it.

Q. Does the fact that they storyboard these cartoons help? I assume you see the storyboard.

A. Well, you have to know what's

Roger's fall through eleven stories at the hospital takes him through every imaginable room.

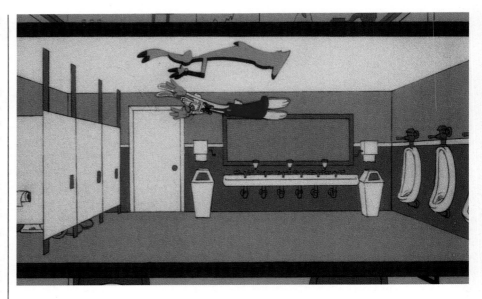

happening to the character to be that character and to react in a situation. So since it's a visual medium, they have to show you a picture of what's going on so that you can conceive of the reaction. And the more detail they can show you, the better. Sometimes it's a reciprocal process. It goes back and forth, where I'll do something and that'll go back to the animators and then that will spark something in them that takes it a step further, where they animate something that wasn't there. And then they'll come back and I'll have to fill in something that they animated that hadn't been voiced before, so it goes back and forth. It's a really unique art form.

Q. Tell us about your background. You're an actor and you've done stand-up, is that correct?

A. I've done stand-up, television and movies—**Welcome Back, Kotter**, **Night Shift**, **Nightmare on Elm Street**—but this was the first thing that made me internationally known.

Q. How did you come to be chosen as the voice of Roger Rabbit?

A. Bob Zemeckis saw me do my stand-up act in a club ten years ago. And he never forgot me and brought me in to do Roger. One of the reasons he hired me was because he knew that there were aspects of my personality that were similar

A scrupulous attention to detail— though often unnoticed by the viewing audience—is typical in the *Roger Rabbit* cartoons. This is evidenced by the fictional 1947 copyright date, below the logo, at the beginning of "Tummy Trouble," which was presented as though produced in the 1940s.

to Roger's.

Q. So it wasn't a question of him having a whole lot of people in mind?

A. No one else was considered.

Q. Are you planning on doing anything with Disney and Touchstone besides the Roger Rabbit projects?

A. Oh, yeah. I have a whole deal there to have my own television show and to star, write, direct, and produce movies.

Q. How else has Roger changed your life? Can you talk about how people react to you? How children react to you?

A. Oh, people see me and say, "There's Roger Rabbit." I don't look or sound like Roger Rabbit, so that's pretty bizarre.

And he really did strike a chord with kids. It's pretty amazing.

Q. Do you have a lot of requests when people do see you to do the voice?

A. Yeah, people ask me that quite frequently.

Q. And is that something you're comfortable doing?

A. As long as they say please.

Q. Do they say, "please," like Roger says please?

A. Well, if they do that, then I definitely do it nicely for them.

Q. How did you develop that kind of trademark, the way Roger pronounces his P's?

A. Well, I was instructed that all great cartoon characters have some kind of speech impediment and realized that if I wanted to keep this job, I'd better come up with something, and that was the only thing I could think of. So it worked.

Q. Is there anything else that you want to convey about Roger or "Tummy Trouble"?

A. Well, about Roger, I think that we won't know the full impact of his popularity for ten years. It takes that much time to really see whether a character has a foothold on society, and I think that Roger does and I think that in ten years you'll really see the effect.